Sorted!

Julie Wilson

First published in Great Britain by Axis Education Ltd.

ISBN 978-1-84618-233-4

Axis Education, PO Box 459
Shrewsbury, SY4 4WZ

Email: enquiries@axiseducation.co.uk
www.axiseducation.co.uk

Hollie had been at Fletcher Road Secondary School for just a few weeks. She was a new Year 7. She'd been nervous about going to high school, but it was all right. She'd made new friends. The lessons were okay. Even the teachers were nice. Everything about new school was fine, except for one thing – the school bus.

Most of Hollie's new friends lived close to the school. They didn't go on the bus. Every day at home-time she had to get all her stuff together – coat, school bag, PE kit and sometimes her cooking – and walk down the drive to queue for the bus. It took her a long time. There were no seats left downstairs, so she had to climb up to the top deck. Hollie hated the top deck.

Sorted!

They were told where to sit. Not by teachers, by Year 9s. The Year 9s on the bus were evil. In school, most of them were just like everyone else, but on the bus they turned into something else – bossy, loud and scary.

None of Hollie's classmates took her bus, so she had on her own. In the first week of school, Hollie had sat down on a seat in the middle of the bus. She was staring out of the window when a Year 9 girl had come from the back of the bus.

'Oy!' the girl shouted, right in Hollie's face.

Hollie recognised her. She was one of the pupils that had shown new starters around the school before the summer holidays.

'What do you think you're doing?' said the girl.

'Nothing,' said Hollie.

'Get out of that seat!' the girl said. Her face was still right up close to Hollie's.

'Why?' Hollie asked. She had no idea what this was about.

''Cos it's a Year 8 seat, stupid!' The girl pointed to the front of the bus. 'You lot sit there!'

The girl was so scary that Hollie did as she was told.

★★★★

It got worse as the term went on. The top deck was a place for the girls to hang out with the boys and for the boys to show off. The Year 7s had to sit and be quiet while the older kids had fights and threw things.

Sometimes the boys would do 'window charging', where they would throw themselves from one side of the bus to the other. A group of them would run across the bus from side to side, bashing the windows each time. They said they were trying to make the bus topple over.

The noise was always terrible. One day, as the Year 9s were window charging, the bus swerved at a roundabout. Hollie's bag fell off her seat. The older kids cheered, but for the Year 7s it was scary. The bus driver stopped the bus. The kids could hear him panting as he stomped up the stairs. He was red in the face.

'Sit down you lot and shut up!' he shouted.
'All this running around up here is too much.
You'll make me crash! There's enough seats
for you. So just sit down.'

When he'd gone, they burst out laughing.

'Who's he to tell us what to do?' Tasha
shouted. The other Year 9s nodded.

Hollie knew that it didn't matter what the
driver said – nothing was going to stop them.
She was right – the minute he started up the
engine, the older kids just carried on with
what they had been doing.

Every day, by the time Hollie reached her
stop, there were bottles, cans and food all
over the floor. The Year 9's often used the
younger kids as target practice, so most of
the rubbish ended up at the front. The top
deck looked like a war zone, but it looked as

if the Year 7s had made the mess. More than once, Hollie had picked up her bag and found it covered in yoghurt or coke.

****

Sorted!

Hollie told her mum about the school bus.

'I'm sorry, love,' said her mum, 'but you have to go on the bus. I can't get you there in the car. I work on the other side of town.'

'Can't I get the normal bus?' asked Hollie.

Her mum shook her head. 'I can't afford the bus fare,' she said.

'Can't I walk, then? Please?'

'Walk? It's three and a half miles! You'd be dead by the time you got there.'

'I'm going to get killed, anyway,' said Hollie.

'Don't be dramatic,' said her mum.

But she wasn't being dramatic. This was real.

★★★★

Sorted!

Hollie wasn't the only person who had a problem with the school bus. The Head, Mrs Cope, felt the same way. She had tried everything. She'd had safety staff in to talk to the children. She'd even had teachers patrolling the bus. Things did get better for a while, but then the seating rule started.

The Head knew all about it. Year 9s to the back, Year 8s to the middle and Year 7s at the front. Mrs Cope also knew which children were to blame. Robert Cropper, Tasha Lee, Dan Clarke were names that came up a lot. She had lost count of the detentions she had given them for their school bus behaviour. But it was the other Year 9s that worried her most. These young people were fine in school. They were helpful, happy, keen. And yet, once they got on the bus they changed. They became totally different people. It was not acceptable.

There was only one thing left that she could do. She needed to get the parents on side. Some of them had already spoken to her about the bus. Some Year 7 parents had emailed her with their worries. Mrs Cope didn't want to say that their children were the Year 8s and Year 9s of the future. That their little darlings would one day be ruling the bus if something wasn't done.

She decided to hold a meeting. A letter went out to the parents of all users of the bus. It was clear. She needed their help.

★★★★

The day the letter went out, Tasha Lee was in charge of the bus. She hadn't read the letter. Nor had the Year 8 who refused to move from the back of the top deck. It was Josie Hicks. Hollie knew her. She was hard in school, but Hollie had never seen her being hard on the bus before. Hollie did not think it was such a good idea. If Josie thought she was hard, Tasha was ten times worse.

'Get out of that seat, or I'll slap you,' Tasha said to Josie.

'No,' Josie replied, staring at her.

Tasha did not need an invitation. She lunged at Josie and grabbed her hair, before banging her head against the window. They were both on the floor by the time the driver got upstairs.

'Stop!' he shouted. He must have already

Sorted!

phoned the school because two teachers were close behind him on the stairs. They managed to each pull a girl off the floor.

Tasha and Josie were both bleeding from the head and mouth. Josie had a nose bleed as well. It was a job to keep them apart – they were shouting and swearing at each other, and trying to break free. The driver got off and walked up to a waiting Mrs Cope.

'This is the third fight in a month,' he said. 'I'll have to report it.'

'I realise that, Vin,' said Mrs Cope. 'I've called the parents to a meeting. Will you come too?'

Vin looked pale. 'I don't hold out much hope for this lot,' he said. 'They're like animals on the bus. But I guess it's worth a try.'

Hollie watched Mrs Cope follow Josie and Tasha into school. The Year 7s around her were excited.

'Bitch fight!' one of them said. Hollie said nothing. She was no geek, but she couldn't see how a bitch fight was something to get excited about.

****

The meeting took place on the following Monday. It was full. Mrs Cope was surprised to see how many parents had turned up. Many of them were angry.

'What kind of school is this?' shouted one of them. 'My son's too scared to use the school bus. It's costing me an arm and a leg for him to go by public transport.'

'My child comes home in tears most nights,' another said. 'The other week, the Year 9s took her cooking and tipped it onto the floor. It can't go on.'

The parents were right, thought Mrs Cope. It couldn't go on.

Mrs Cope told the parents that the school was close to losing the bus. The bus company had given Fletcher Road one last chance. Losing the bus would be bad both for the school and for the families.

'I've had a talk with the regular driver, Vin,' she told them, 'but we're going to need your help.' She turned to the driver. 'Vin? Will you please tell everyone what you have in mind?'

Vin got up and told the parents his idea.

★★★★

Hollie looked at the clock in the classroom. Ten to three. At least it was Friday. Only one more bus journey, then the weekend could begin.

When the bell went, she packed up her things and said goodbye to her friends. There was no point in hurrying. She never made the bottom deck. Walking down the drive, she could already hear the noise from the bus.

Hollie got on and climbed the stairs. She was pleased to see that there was a place next to another Year 7 – Kate Holland. At least there'd be someone to sit with.

'All right?' asked Hollie.

'Yeah. Are you?'

'Yeah.'

But they both knew the other one was lying.

The bus hadn't gone far when something hit Hollie on the back of the head. As it bounced off and landed on the floor, she saw that it was an apple core – a large one. It hurt. She held her head. She could feel the tears coming. Kate looked at her.

'You okay?' Kate whispered.

She looked scared. Hollie nodded. She must not cry. She must not turn around. If she did, they'd be ready for her. The shouting was really loud now. Then something happened.

The bus was meant to turn into Broom Lane, but carried on up Station Road instead. As soon as the older kids realised, they stopped what they were doing. Then they started shouting again.

'Hey! You've gone the wrong way!'

'Are you lost?'

'Why don't you get a map, Grandad?'

'He don't know where he's going, innit?'

But the driver just kept going. Hollie was worried. She didn't know the area they were in.

'Is this a new route?' Kate whispered.

'I don't know,' said Hollie. Her head hurt and now they were lost. Great.

Finally, they turned into a large car park. It was a superstore. The driver drove up to some parked cars.

'What's the matter, driver?' shouted one of

the kids. 'You got to get some milk?'

And then, bit by bit, the shouting stopped.
Outside, people were getting out of their
cars. Someone swore.

'What's she doing here?'

'Oh my God!'

They heard the bus doors swish open and
someone get on. Everyone went back to their
seats. A woman came up to the top deck
and looked down the bus. Seeing what she
was looking for, she pointed, then beckoned
with her finger.

'Dylan Smith,' she said, 'get down here!'

A red-faced Year 9 got out of his seat and
walked down to the front. When he got there,
he said in a low voice:

Sorted!

'Mum! You're embarrassing me.'

'Embarrassing you?' she said loudly. 'How do you think I feel? Being rung up and told that my son is behaving like an animal on the school bus! You're meant to be doing your GCSEs next year – if they'll still let you, that is. C'mon.'

She took him down the stairs. There was more laughter and a bit of shouting, along with promises of lots of ribbing the next day. Then another adult got on and came upstairs, and all went quiet, except for one boy.

This time the passenger was a man. The boy who had been shouting and laughing stopped. The man looked at him.

'Have you finished?'

The boy said nothing.

'Or would you like me to tell everybody on the bus what you sleep with at night?'

'Dad!'

'Down here, now.'

Tasha's mum was the scariest. Everyone turned to watch as she stomped down the bus and grabbed Tasha by the arm.

'No more phone, no more laptop, no more ipod,' she told Tasha as they walked to the front of the bus.

'Yeah, right,' said Tasha, looking hard.

'And no more Midsomer Murders,' said her mum.

'Mum!' Tasha screamed.

'Answer me back like that and see what you get,' yelled Tasha's mum as they disappeared down the stairs.

Everybody relaxed a little. For a few seconds, nobody else came up to the top deck. Then there was the sound of heavy footsteps and a tall, large man appeared. Nobody was laughing this time. It was as if the whole bus was holding its breath. Hollie watched, wide-eyed, as he stood there, staring towards the back of the bus. Without a word, Cropper got up and followed the man down the steps.

One by one, eight Year 9s were taken off the bus by a parent. Hollie's head began to feel a whole lot better. The bus was like it had never been before – calm!

★★★★

Sorted!

Mrs Cope was in one of the cars at the superstore. She watched the children being taken off the bus by their parents. She saw how shame-faced they were. When they'd all been taken off, Vin gave her the thumbs up. He looked years younger as he drove off towards the car park exit.

★★★★

'I've seen it all before,' Vin had told Mrs Cope on the day of Tasha and Josie's fight. 'Perhaps we need to do the same as Freewood Comprehensive,' he said.

When Vin told Mrs Cope the plan, she was unsure. Asking the parents to help out like that might not go down so well. Many of them saw it as the school's job to teach their children how to behave.

To her surprise, the parents had been very keen. They thought it was a great idea. By the end of the meeting, everyone seemed happier.

'Sorted!' said a smiling Vin to Mrs Cope when the hall was empty.

'We'll see,' she had said.

Sorted!

Only time would tell if the problem really had been sorted, but Mrs Cope couldn't deny that she was hopeful.

★★★★